PLANTS
Extinction
or Survival?

PLANTS,

Extinction

or Survival?

Howard and
Margery Facklam

ENSLOW PUBLISHERS, INC.

Bloy St. & Ramsey Ave.   P.O. Box 38
Box 777   Aldershot
Hillside, NJ 07205   Hants GU12 6BP
U.S.A.   U.K.

Copyright © 1990 by Howard and Margery Facklam

Library of Congress Cataloging-in-Publication Data

Facklam, Howard.
    Plants: extinction or survival? / Howard Facklam and Margery Facklam.
        p. cm.
    Includes bibliographical references.
    Summary: Describes the importance of germplasm and how storage banks around the world are preserving plant seeds so that plant species will not be lost through disease and environmental conditions.

        ISBN 0-89490-248-2

    1. Crops—Germplasm resources—Juvenile literature 2. Germplasm resources, Plant—Juvenile literature 3. Plant conservation—Juvenile literature 4. Plants—Extinction—Juvenile literature. [1. Germplasm resources, Plant. 2. Plant conservation. 3. Seeds—Protection.] I. Facklam, Margery. II. Title.

SB123.3.F33 1990   89-17038
333.95'316—dc20   CIP
                                                      AC

Printed in the United States of America
10 9 8 7 6 5 4 3 2

Illustration Credits:
Dr. Barbara McClintock (photographer David Micklos): p. 43; Forest Service Collection, National Agricultural Library: pp. 27, 74; Howard Facklam: p. 20; Library of Congress: pp. 10, 13; Marcos Santilli: pp. 51, 55; Merle H. Jensen, University of Arizona: p. 17; National Archives: p. 29; National Portrait Gallery, Smithsonian Institution: p. 36; National Seed Storage Laboratory, Fort Collins, CO: pp. 60, 62; New York State Agricultural Experiment Station, Geneva, NY: pp. 40, 45, 65; Paul Facklam: pp. 19, 31, 37, 54, 75, 81, 83; Photo by T. Plowman: p. 33; ©RBG, Kew: pp. 24, 67; The Upjohn Co.: p. 87

for our children
Thomas, David, John, Paul, and Margaret

Acknowledgments

Nonfiction writers need help, especially in digging out the facts about a subject as complex and important as the basic food on earth—the plants.

We are grateful for the help of experts who were so generous with their valuable time, especially Dr. Philip Forsline, curator of the National Clonal Germplasm Repository for Apples and Grapes; John Williams, director of Communication Services at the New York State Agriculture Extension Station of Cornell University; Dr. Richard Shultes, Harvard University Botanical Gardens; Dr. Merle Jensen, assistant dean of the College of Agriculture, University of Arizona; and Joan Kilmer, garden writer and good friend.

—*Howard and Margery Facklam*

Contents

1

The Potato That Changed the World

"Six famished and ghastly skeletons, to all appearances dead, were huddled in a corner on some filthy straw, their sole covering what seemed a ragged horse cloth, and their wretched legs hanging out. I approached in horror, and found them alive, four children, a woman, and one once a man."

An Irish justice of the peace saw that dreadful scene at a farm in Ireland during the potato famine of 1845. It was a time when lush green fields turned brown in a matter of weeks, filling the air with the putrid smell of rotting plants decaying into slime. Three-quarters of Ireland's potato crop was wiped out by a fungus called *Phytophthora infestans* during a long stretch of cold, damp weather in which this fungus thrives. Within a few years, more than a million people died of starvation, and millions more left the country. Today, most of the people of Irish descent in the United States and Canada came from families who emigrated during the potato famine.

How could the loss of just one crop change the course of history

BOY AND GIRL AT CAHERA.

This old illustration from an Irish newspaper shows two children who were victims of the potato famine.

as it did? The deadly combination of situations began with a single strain of potato called the "lumper."

Potatoes were not native to Ireland. They came from Peru and spread throughout Europe when Spanish explorers brought this single strain back from South America. Nobody knew that the lumper, so easily grown, so full of nutrition, would be easy prey to the blight fungus in the damp climate of Ireland. Had there been several different kinds of potatoes, one of them might have been immune to that blight. But that wasn't the case.

And then the political situation in Ireland also worked against the peasants. They owned no land, but worked as tenant farmers, raising wheat, corn, oats, cattle, pigs, and poultry for wealthy landowners, who shipped most of the food to England. On less than an acre of the poorest land on the farm, each tenant family was allowed to raise food for themselves. They planted almost nothing but potatoes, not because they loved potatoes overly much but because this crop provided the most nutrition in the least space. Someone figured that a farmer ate about twelve pounds of potatoes each day, his wife ate eight pounds, and each child used five pounds. Nothing went to waste. Leftovers fed the chickens and the family pig. Every farm family raised a pig, but it was neither family food nor pet. "Paddy's pig" was the "gift" to the landowner for the year's rent. When the potato crop failed, the chickens and pigs died, and the people starved.

But the potato famine is history. A crop failure can't hurt a nation now, not with supermarkets piled high with more kinds of food than the world has ever seen—or can it?

We are a planet of plant eaters. No one knows exactly how many different kinds of plants exist on earth. The best estimate is 240,000 species. Scientists guess there may be more than 15,000 species yet to be discovered. Only 5,000 have been studied in any detail. But the real surprise is that there are fewer than three dozen crops that feed the world! And the "big four" are wheat, corn, rice, and potatoes. It's as though we're shopping in a huge supermarket and buying just one or two items. Imagine what would happen to that long line of cereal boxes, pastas, and baked goods at the supermarket if wheat should be wiped out?

There have been some close calls. In 1916, Canada lost 100 million bushels of wheat and the United States lost 200 million bushels to a microscopic fungus called red rust. The wheat shortage was so bad that the federal government asked Americans to have two wheatless days each week and to eat cornbread instead.

A disease called the Victoria blight wiped out most of America's oat crop in 1946, even though farmers had used thirty varieties of oat seeds. But all thirty came from a common parent, and that parent had passed along its susceptibility to the blight.

America lost almost half its corn in the southern states in 1970, enough corn to feed the cattle that would have produced 30 billion quarter-pound hamburgers! Most of that corn had come from a single Texas variety, and the genetic defect was passed along. We didn't suffer in North America as the Irish did, of course, because we had other food crops available to everyone. But the important similarity between the Irish potato and the American corn is the "narrow genetic diversity." It's a vital point, and it means that all the corn planted in the 1970s came from identical germplasm, as all the Irish potatoes had come from identical germplasm.

An Oregon farmer said it best. "You can take away the tractor, the fertilizer, the irrigation pipe, and the combine. You can burn down the barn and pull up the fences and still be a farmer. But take away the seed, those minute bits of germplasm planted in the fields, and you might as well try growing rocks."

Genes carry the blueprint for the plant. The collection of genes in each cell of a plant determines what it will look like and how it will grow. But germplasm is more than just genes. It's been called the "stuff of life." It's everything within the plant or seed that determines the traits and characteristics of that plant. Germplasm is not just the DNA in the nucleus of the cell but the whole cell, the whole seed, the whole plant.

Germplasm can't be measured. It can't even be precisely defined. We talk about the germplasm of a grape, or the germplasm of all Niagara white grapes, or the germplasm of all the grapes grown in New York State. Plant germplasm may be a seed, but it can also be a cutting—a small piece of leaf or root or twig—pieces of a plant's tissue. Or it can be DNA in genes suspended in nutrient broth in a test tube.

No matter what form it takes, germplasm consists of combinations of genes, and every cell of every plant (or animal) holds these combinations. If a plant is characterized by 10,000 genes, then each cell in that plant has 10,000 genes. Multiply those 10,000 genes carried in the millions of cells of a plant, and you can see that each plant has billions of genes.

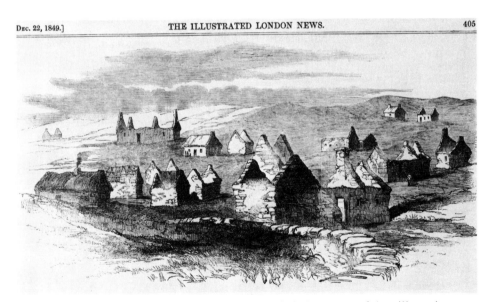

An issue of the *Illustrated London News* in 1849 shows one of the villages in Ireland abandoned during the years of the potato famine.

Even though the plans for a new plant are passed along in genes from one generation to the next, the plans are not turned on or "expressed" in every plant. Environmental factors can change things. A seed planted in moist, fertile soil and exposed to long, sunny days may express a different group of genes from a similar seed planted in dry, claylike soil and exposed to long stretches of rainy weather.

When the weather was good in Ireland, it didn't matter that the lumper potato had no built-in or genetic resistance to the blight fungus, but when the weather changed and the fungus spread, it certainly did matter. Even now, too many of our crops are vulnerable to disease because they don't have diversity of germplasm.

Every plant alive today, whether rice from Rangoon or sunflowers from Iowa, is a kind of living history of germplasm passed from one generation to the next through the ages. It's not possible to trace germplasm to its exact origin because it's always changing, moving, mixing. Steven Witt, author of *Biotechnology and Genetic Diversity*, says, "Tracking a portion of germplasm through history is like tracking a gallon of sea water through history. It can't be done."

Maybe we can't track it, but we can protect it. Germplasm is the world's most valuable resource, more precious than gold, uranium, or oil.

Even though we know there are more than 2,000 species of potatoes, we still depend upon one species from which we get twelve varieties for 85 percent of the world's harvest. The sameness of most of the world's potatoes makes them easily susceptible to diseases.

By the year 2000, there may be six billion people to feed on this planet. We'll need to double food production in the next ten years. Can we do it? Will we learn in time to use new and different plants for their rich, untapped germplasm?

2

The Battle for Survival

Stop taking care of your lawn. Don't mow, water, fertilize, or weed it, and in a few years it won't be a lawn anymore but a place where the wild things grow. Crab grass, dandelions, chickory, and other weeds will take over. These are nature's survivors. The adapations they have evolved over thousands and millions of years give them just a little bit better chance to live. Charles Darwin said it best when he called it "survival of the fittest."

A plant's first battle is the competition with other plants for light, water, and nutrients. One way to get more light is to grow taller. In doing that, soft green stems evolve into thick, woody stems that can support leaves over 200 feet above the ground, like the Ponderosa pine, shading all others below.

Ivy, wild grape, and other vines evolved into climbers as a way of rising above other plants to find the sun. The kudzu vine, which was introduced into the United States from Japan in the 1930s, was planted across the southern states in an effort to control erosion. Today it is known as the curse of the south. In a single season the kudzu can grow seventy-five feet, and wherever its stem touches the ground, it can take root and create new climbers that eventually smother the trees and cover all the vegetation they grow on.

The second battle is for water and the nutrients dissolved in it. Plants called epiphytes have developed ways to grow on the surfaces of other plants, absorbing minerals and moisture that falls on the leaves of their hosts. Staghorn ferns, Spanish moss, and many species of orchids are epiphytes found mainly in the tropics.

Most plants, of course, draw water from the soil through their roots. In order to get enough nutrients, a rye plant two feet tall may have 14 million branches in its root system with a combined length of some 380 miles. Plants such as the carrot have long taproots that reach deep into the soil; others such as the cactus spread shallow roots over a wide area to absorb water quickly from the sometimes heavy but infrequent rains. Cactuses and some of their relatives have adapted fleshy stems and branches where water can be stored during long droughts. A botanist in California uprooted a cactus plant and placed it on his laboratory bench. During the experiment, the cactus received light but no water, except from the air or what it had stored in its fleshy leaves. At the end of six years, it was still alive.

Most land plants are killed by salt water, but a few species called halophytes have evolved genes that allow them to grow despite the salt. Pickleweed, Palmer's grass, and saltwort are examples of halophytes that thrive in salt marshlands where there is less competition from other vegetation.

It's long been known that many kinds of plants cannot grow around the base of a walnut tree, but only recently have botanists found out why. The walnut tree produces a toxic substance called juglone, which prevents the growth of other plants. This, of course, assures plenty of water and nutrients for the walnut tree.

Plants carry on a kind of chemical warfare against other plants. In 1980, two Canadian ecologists discovered that the balsam poplar tree makes a chemical that specifically prevents the growth of a would-be competitor, the green alder tree. The decaying leaves of a shrub in the daisy family release a substance in the soil that prevents the germination of seeds of other plants, thereby assuring the survival of its own seeds. Guayule, the rubber plant, makes a chemical that inhibits the growth of its *own* seeds, which may seem strange, but in this way each tree is allowed to take advantage of the nutrients it needs. In a rubber plantation, seedlings grow only outside the circle of the mother plant's root system.

This ability of one plant to produce chemicals to kill or inhibit the growth of another plant is called allelopathy. Botanists expect they will find many more examples of allelopathy as they investigate the ecological roles of more plants.

Compared to animals, of course, plants may seem like defenseless organisms. They are grazed upon by cattle, goats, deer, and other large herbivores. They are eaten by smaller mammals and

In fields flooded by salt water, like this one on a farm in Puerto Panasco, Mexico, farmers are experimenting with halophyte crops.

insects and are blighted by fungi, bacteria, and viruses. But against all these predators, some plants have built a remarkable arsenal.

Blackberries and raspberries have thorny stems that grow in a dense mass that keeps away the herbivores. The prickly toothed leaves of the thistle, the coarse, stinging hairs of the nettle, and the spines of cactus, holly, and some palms are unpleasant to the soft mouth and lip tissue of grazing animals.

Animals don't eat poison ivy, poison sumac, or the giant hogweed because of their bitter taste. The sand grasses and sawgrass of Florida aren't eaten because they contain silica, which has the taste of gritty sand. A tough outer cuticle makes the yucca, aloe, and century plants also difficult to chew.

But even as plants developed such defenses, some animals evolved methods to counteract them. The giraffe, with its flexible lips and long tongue, can pick out the leaves from between the long spines of the acacia tree. The land iguana from the Galapagos Islands can eat the spiny fruit and thick, padded leaves of the *Opuntia* cactus with ease because it rolls the fruit on the ground to break off the spines. Then the iguana holds the pod with one foot and uses the claws of the other foot to break off the spines on the fleshy leaf pads.

But the biggest predator of plants is not the largest of animals. It's the smallest. Insects such as the locusts of Africa and the gypsy moth in the United States can as easily wipe out acres of plants as they can destroy a single one. Much of a plant's arsenal is aimed at these, the most deadly of their predators.

In the leaves of white clover and its cousin the bird's-foot trefoil, there are chemicals called cyanogenic glycosides. When the leaves of these plants are chewed or damaged, the glycosides break down and release small amounts of free cyanide, which is fatal to insects, slugs, and snails. If you crush a leaf of the white clover or trefoil, you can smell the faint odor of bitter almond, which is the warning smell of cyanide. Members of the cabbage family,

The prickly spines on the leaves of the thistle are good as armor to protect the plant from grazing cattle and other large herbivores.

including broccoli, cauliflower, turnip, and radish, contain a different glycoside called sinigrin, which is also poisonous to many insects.

The most common of the bitter-tasting substances in plants is a group of chemicals called tannins, which are used to tan leather. A high concentration of tannin not only gives a plant a disagreeable taste but also makes the plant less nutritious for an insect. Combined with the plant's proteins, the tannins form a compound that can't be digested by insects. Winter moth caterpillars feed on oak leaves in spring, but in June, when the tannin content in those leaves rises, the caterpillars stop eating them.

Other plants make chemicals that prevent digestion of their proteins, but these chemicals are made only when the plant is attacked. When chewing insects go to work on a tomato plant, a substance is released in the plant tissue that signals it to begin

The Galapagos land iguana rolls the fleshy leaf or pad of a cactus along the ground to break off the long spines before eating it.

making that protective chemical. The Sitka willow tree has an unusual system when insects begin to chew on its leaves. Not only does the food value of the leaves decrease, but the food value of leaves in nearby willow trees also deteriorates. Scientists think that the attacked tree may send some kind of chemical signal through the air that warns neighboring trees to prepare for the insects. Richard Karhan, at the University of California, discovered that when spider mites feed on the first early leaves of a young cotton plant, the leaves that appear later produce a chemical that makes the plant resistant to any further attack by the spider mites.

The catnip plant makes a chemical that for some reason attracts cats, but more important for the plant, it repels beetles and ants. Strangely enough, some plants have evolved a way to attract ants for their own protection. Ants seem to love the nectar of the aspen sunflower, and while they're collecting that nectar, they destroy other insects who happen along. Although the ants are protecting their own food source, the sunflower seeds are protected from insects until the seeds are mature enough to ensure the next generation.

Of all the major organisms that destroy plants—viruses, bacteria, and fungi—the fungi are most common. Corn and wheat blight are caused by a fungus, and Dutch elm disease begins with a fungus carried by a beetle. The presence of a disease organism in the tissues of a plant stimulates that plant to make chemicals called phytoalexins. *Phyto* comes from a Greek word meaning plant, and *alexein* meaning to ward off. These chemicals ward off or inhibit the growth of fungi and bacteria, working much like our own immune system, where the presence of a foreign invader (the disease organism) triggers our white blood cells to attack with antibodies. A plant's ability to survive depends upon its ability to make enough of these phytoalexins fast enough to destroy the disease. The first phytoalexin was discovered in peas in 1960. Since then others have been found in peppers, clover, beans, and apples.

The ability to make chemicals for protection against predators probably evolved millions of years ago in the weeds that were the ancestors of our crop plants. There seems to be a vast undiscovered arsenal of chemical-producing genes in plants. It is these genes for survival that the plant hunters are searching for and that plant breeders are trying to develop in our cultivated plants to strengthen them for our own survival.

3

The Plant Hunters

Shivering and soaked to the skin, David Douglas unloaded his collections from his horse's saddlebags. With care he checked the pouches he'd filled with roots, seeds, and whole plants, hoping the weather had not damaged them. Since morning he'd traveled thirty miles on foot through rain and sleet in the rough wilds of Canada, while the horse carried his equipment and collections. Before he slept that night, Douglas wrote in his journal that for days he'd not been dry or warm, he'd had little to eat, and under the circumstances, he said, "I am liable to become fretful."

Plant collecting has never been for the weak-willed or timid, but it was a profession made for David Douglas. Born in Scotland in 1789, the son of a village stonemason, Douglas left school when he was only ten to become a gardener's apprentice. When he finished each day's chores, he hiked through nearby fields, collecting, classifying, and pressing plants. Often he'd transplant unusual specimens in his father's garden. He read every book he could find on natural history and travel, but his real passion was botany. He knew he would become a botanist, but not a stay-at-home, microscope-using kind. He wanted to be a plant

David Douglas was one of the famous plant hunters from England. The great Douglas fir tree is named in his honor.

hunter and travel to far places to bring back species unknown in England.

By the time Douglas was twenty, he was working at the Botanical Gardens in Glasgow, where he formed a lasting friendship with William Hooker, who was professor of botany at the University of Glasgow and would shortly become director of the famed Royal Botanical Gardens at Kew. Together Hooker and Douglas searched the Scottish Highlands for new plant varieties, and through Hooker's recommendation David Douglas's dream came true. The Horticultural Society of London appointed Douglas as plant collector, with an assignment to travel to the eastern part of the United States of America to collect specimens of fruit trees.

After a grueling fifty-nine days at sea from Liverpool to New York, Douglas then traveled by stagecoach, foot, and horse-drawn canal boat through New York State, collecting seeds, roots, and whole plants. The night he arrived in Albany, the state's capital city was celebrating the opening of the Erie Canal. But instead of joining the boisterous crowds for fireworks and parades, Douglas stayed in his hotel room, drying and pressing the plants he'd collected that day.

On that first trip, Douglas added so many plants to the Royal Botanical Gardens' collection that six months later he was sent on one of the biggest, most profitable expeditions to collect along the Columbia River in British Columbia, Canada.

The eight-month voyage took him across the Atlantic, around the tip of South America, with a brief stop at the Galapagos Islands on the equator off the coast of Ecuador, and up the western coast of the United States. From his base at Vancouver, Canada, Douglas traveled 2,000 miles that first summer along the Columbia River south into the Cascade Mountains of the United States. It was not an easy trip! He carried little personal gear in order to have room for more than a hundred pounds of botanical paper used for drying and pressing plants. Several times Douglas was so hungry that he was forced to eat some of the seeds and roots he'd worked so hard to collect. On a trip down a tributary of the Columbia, rocks ripped a hole in the bottom of his canoe, and several weeks' worth of collecting were washed away. One night, burning with fever, hungry, and cold, he was awakened by a gnawing sound—pack rats were eating his seeds and roots.

But it was on that exhausting trip to the Northwest that Douglas discovered the majestic tree that bears his name, the Douglas fir. In two years, Douglas sent several shiploads of conifers and other plants back to England, including the digger pine, western white pine, ponderosa pine, silver fir, and the tallest, the sugar pine. In a letter to his friend, Professor Hooker, Douglas wrote, "You will begin to think I have manufactured pines at my pleasure."

When he arrived home, David Douglas found that he was famous. He had set a record by introducing more plants into England than had ever been collected by one person from one country.

Not all plant collectors have experienced such rigorous and dangerous trips as Douglas's. But Sir Joseph Banks, who trained collectors for the Royal Botanical Gardens at Kew, told his students that plant collecting required single-mindedness, stamina, and a cheerful indifference to heat or cold, thirst or hunger, tropical fevers, revolting diseases, shipwrecking, or even death. He knew what he was talking about. He had endured all those things but death as botanist aboard Captain Cook's ship *Endeavor*.

In the 1700s and 1800s it was customary to send a naturalist along on any exploration of a new territory, or even on extended trading voyages. Charles Darwin was the naturalist aboard the H.M.S. *Beagle* for two years, charged with collecting plant, animal, and mineral specimens wherever the ship dropped anchor. It was on this voyage that Darwin collected much of his data for his world-shaking theory of evolution. But most of the early plant

David Douglas discovered pines like this 198.5-foot-tall ponderosa in the Columbia National Forest.

hunters were only looking for medicinal herbs or exotic plants for the gardens of Europe.

The first record of a plant expedition is carved in the temple garden walls belonging to Hatshepsut, who was queen of Egypt in 1482 B.C. She sent five ships to the land of Punt in East Africa to bring back seeds or specimens of the boswellia tree, which produces gum from which frankincense is made. Thirty-one trees survived the voyage.

Many of Charlemagne's Crusaders carried home aromatic herbs for new medicines or new flavors. It was becoming popular to cover up the odors of the unsanitary conditions of cities with the more pleasant odor of herbs. Missionaries and diplomats sent home to Europe a steady supply of new and unusual plants. In the 1600s, Henry Comptom, Bishop of England, instructed his clergymen to ship back plants from their foreign posts, and it wasn't long before he had one of the largest collections of exotic and ornamental plants in England. In one year, DeBubecq, a Flemish ambassador to the Court of Constantinople, introduced into Europe the horse chestnut tree, the lilac, the mock orange, and many varieties of tulips.

The seventeenth century gardens of the wealthy people of England and Europe were not kept so much for raising food as for show. So eager were European nurserymen for new plants that they had agents at the docks to buy plants brought home by sailors. It is said that the tuber of one unusual dahlia flower was exchanged for a diamond.

With the worldwide population explosion that began with the twentieth century, collectors increased their efforts to find plants that would be a source of medicines and food. The search was on for grains, vegetables, and fruits that might be resistant to diseases, pests, and extremes of cold and drought. It became such a high priority that, in 1918, the United States Department of Agriculture appointed Frank Meyer to the first post as Economic Plant Collector. He was sent to China to hunt along the Yangtze River for

In 1918, Frank Meyer was appointed to the post of the nation's first official economic plant collector.

hardy varieties of rice, beans, and fruit that could be grown in North America. He made four expeditions through the great plains of China and into eastern Russia, Manchuria, and Korea. The germplasm he collected is still found in many of our crops. Since that time, thousands of men and women have been sent out by governments, universities, and seed and pharmaceutical companies in search of new germplasm.

One of the most prolific plant hunters in history was a Russian, Nikolai Vavilov. From 1920 to 1940, he headed the Lenin All-Union Academy of Agricultural Sciences. With 20,000 employees, Vavilov built the world's most extensive plant collection, including 50,000 species of wildflowers, 31,000 samples of wheat, and 2,800 samples of corn. After years of exploration, Vavilov concluded that there are nine major and three minor regions of the world from which all the important crops originated. Now known as the Vavilov Centers, these regions contain the wild and weedy relatives of our crop plants and the primitive cultivated varieties we call "land races." Land races are plants once cultivated by primitive agricultural methods. They have evolved through thousands of years as they adapted to whatever new environments people took them to. Every time a land race is discovered, it's as though a new book were added to a library.

Potatoes were cultivated more than 8,000 years ago in the Andes Mountains. Each year the farmers selected the strongest, healthiest plants and saved their seeds for the next year's planting. Through centuries of this selection, thousands of different varieties or land races of potatoes have developed. Each variety may have a slightly different adaptation to withstand a specific group of diseases or an adaptation to grow at a certain altitude or in a certain kind of soil. One botanist found forty-six varieties of potatoes growing in one small field in Peru. Nothing like the Irish potato famine is likely to happen to Peruvians. From the International Potato Center in Lima, Peru, collectors continue to go out to search

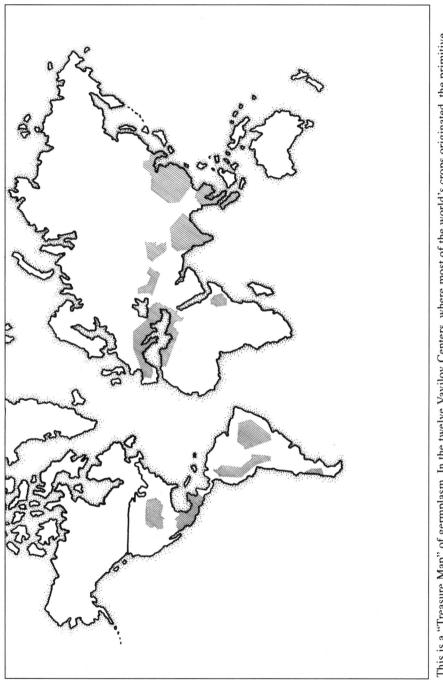

This is a "Treasure Map" of germplasm. In the twelve Vavilov Centers, where most of the world's crops originated, the primitive cultivated varieties are still growing.

the mountains of Peru, Ecuador, and Chile for the primitive ancestors of those cultivated potatoes in order to preserve that germplasm.

All over the world, scientists seek land races before they are lost forever. Already many of the land races of wheat in Greece are extinct. The ancestors of red wheat in North America came from Greek varieties, and plant hunters hope to find ancient varieties that still survive. The long drought in Ethiopia may have already destroyed all the ancient varieties of wheat and barley.

In 1960, a team of plant hunters from the Massachusetts Institute of Technology began to study the food plants of Central America. At the end of five years, they had found 203 species of wild, edible vegetables never before used as food.

The search is on for food plants that can grow in poor soil or arid climates. Nations may be forced to turn to different foods if their cornfields continue to turn brown from drought or their wheat is wiped out by cold as the world's climates shift.

Dr. Gary Nabhan and his graduate students at the University of Arizona hunt remote canyons of Arizona and Mexico for different varieties of tepary beans, which were once cultivated by Indians of the Southwest. High in protein and well adapted to the desert environment, the tepary beans could become a major food crop for the arid and semiarid regions of Africa.

Dr. Richard Shultes, from the Harvard University Botanical Museum, has spent more than forty years searching for medicinal plants. For fourteen of those years he lived among Indian tribes of the Amazon basin and learned from their skilled medicine men. Dr. Shultes has collected more than 24,000 plants. In the early years, Shultes watched the Indians use gum from a tree to treat fungus infections of the skin. Forty years later in another part of the Amazon, he saw Indians doing the same thing. Since then, Brazilian chemists have found three new compounds in this gum with antifungal properties. Dr. Shultes is convinced that collecting plants already in use by different groups of people for the same purpose will ultimately lead to new medicines.

The plant hunter's treasures are the plant breeder's raw materials. Collections of previously unknown species are used by plant breeders to produce crops with higher yields and greater resistance to the farmer's four enemies—pests, diseases, drought, and cold.

Dr. Richard Shultes in a dugout canoe with the world's largest water lily, with leaves six or seven feet in diameter.

4

The Plant Tamers

The first plant breeder in history was the person who, thousands of years ago, selected seeds to plant the following year. It's likely that he, or she, chose seeds from the sweeter or bigger fruit or an ear of corn with the most kernels, assuming that those seeds would produce the same kind of plants. For centuries farmers have selected seeds from the best plants in their fields, but no one knows when the first farmer deliberately crossed one variety of plant with another for the purpose of a better crop. It may have happened after they had seen the results of crossbreeding their livestock, but whenever or however it began, this kind of selective crossbreeding has been going on for hundreds, possibly thousands, of years.

Among the untold numbers of people who have "tamed" the wild plants to create better crops, the most famous is probably Luther Burbank, known as the "father" of 222 different varieties of trees, fruits, vegetables, and flowers.

Luther Burbank was number thirteen in a family of fifteen children, which may account for the fact that Burbank spent a lot of time outdoors. His career started when he deliberately planted weeds in his father's vegetable garden.

Luther Burbank was one of America's most famous plant breeders.

Burbank was born in 1849 in Lancaster, Massachusetts, where he began his education in a one-room schoolhouse. But his real education took place when his favorite uncle, Professor Levi Burbank, came to visit. The professor, who headed the geology department at the museum of the Boston Society of Natural Sciences, introduced young Burbank to some of the mysteries of nature, but what fascinated Burbank most was the professor's demonstration of grafting. Burbank learned how to make an apple tree produce two different varieties of apples by grafting a branch from one kind of apple tree to a branch of another kind.

When the famous naturalist Louis Agassiz from Harvard University visited the farm with the professor, it changed the course of Luther Burbank's life. From this brilliant scientist, Burbank not only learned how plants reproduce and develop seeds, but also how one plant transfers pollen to another in a process called pollination. In teaching Burbank that crossbreeding can work only in closely

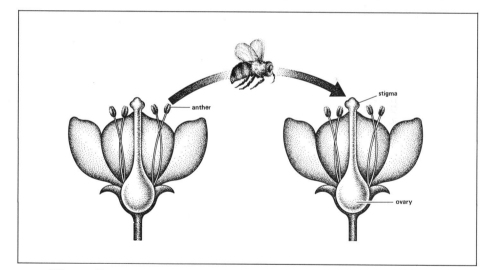

When pollen, containing the male genes produced by the anther of the female plant, is carried on the wind or by insects to the stigma, or female part, of another plant, it's called cross-pollination. When the pollen germinates on the stigma, the sperm travels to the ovary where it fertilizes the egg cells, which develop into seeds.

related plants of the same species or genus, Agassiz suggested that he might experiment with crossbreeding weeds to produce useful plants.

One day Burbank found a ripened seed ball on a potato plant. Potatoes seldom produce ripe seeds in temperate climates, so farmers plant the potato or tuber instead. When Burbank opened the seed ball, he found twenty-three seeds, which he stored through the winter and planted the following spring. Twenty-three different potatoes grew from those seeds, producing mostly small, crooked tubers. But from two of those plants, he got large, smooth, white-fleshed potatoes. Burbank saved the two large potatoes and planted them the following year. One of those produced twice as many new potato tubers as the other plant, and Burbank sold the exclusive rights to develop and sell this variety to a nurseryman for $150. That was a lot of money in 1875, but it turned out to be a real bargain for the nurseryman because that variety, known as the Burbank potato, became the most popular potato grown in the northwestern United States. Its modern descendent, the russet Burbank, is the source of today's McDonald's French fries.

When three of Luther Burbank's brothers moved to California, they wrote to tell him that plants grew year round in the good weather and that his experiments would take less time because he'd be able to grow two generations of plants in the time it took to raise one back east. So with his $150 potato money and some other savings, Burbank left Massachusetts and bought a small parcel of land in Santa Rosa, California, to start his own potato and fruit-tree nursery.

California in 1880 was not yet the great fruit-growing state it is now, and Burbank's business grew slowly. People were not interested at first in new varieties, so Burbank continued to sell ordinary nursery stock while he experimented with crossing plants to get hardier varieties.

By 1911, Burbank had developed a thornless blackberry, a

stoneless plum, and a stoneless prune. During his years in California, he introduced twenty new varieties of plums and an ever-bearing strawberry that was a cross between a plant from Chile and one from the United States. He also produced a spineless cactus that cattle could graze on, ten varieties of dahlias, eleven varieties of roses, and twenty-two different gladiolus bulbs. He gave us hardier, better breeds of squash, rhubarb, peas, corn, asparagus, apples, and cherries. Most breeders specialize in one or two kinds of plants, but Burbank always had experiments going with dozens of different species. His genius was the ability to select from perhaps 10,000 plants the single one with the right characteristics to cross with another to produce the improvement he wanted.

Not too many years before Burbank began mixing and matching plants, an Austrian monk was crossing pea plants in a monastery garden and discovering the fundamental laws of heredity. After Gregor Mendel cross-pollinated tall pea plants with short, or pink with red, he saved the seeds and planted them the following spring. Carefully he examined each new plant for size, color, and other traits. He recorded the results and learned which traits were passed from one generation to another. Gregor Mendel knew nothing about genes or chromosomes, but he knew that somehow the male and female carried messages, and some of these messages were more powerful than others. He called the powerful messages dominant, and the less powerful he named recessive. He saw that some messages would skip a generation and appear in later plantings. Mendel's special contribution—the thing no one had done before—was the careful counting and comparing. For seven years this dedicated monk planted and counted and kept records which began to tell a story that did not change.

Mendel showed that characteristics or traits do not blend into some middle ground. They keep their own identity. The pairs of characteristics, some from each parent, might combine, but they sorted themselves out according to a fixed and predictable set of

39

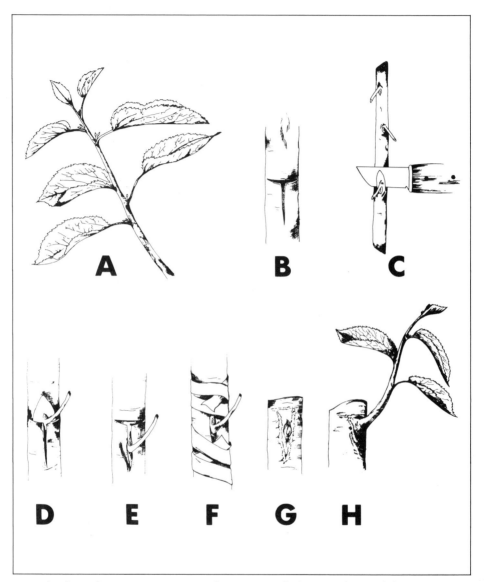

Apples and pears are grown as grafts on rootstocks because they can't be grown from seed. Grafting is done as follows: **A.** The scion, the new variety the breeder wants to reproduce. **B.** The bark of the stock, usually rootstock, has been cut to receive the scion. **C.** After leaves are removed from the scion, the leaf buds are cut off with a sharp knife. **D.E.F.** The leaf bud from the scion is placed in the prepared stock and taped in place. **G.H.** After the rootstock has healed, the new variety grows on the rootstock.

rules. Although this set of rules—the laws of heredity—did not become known and accepted until 1900, it did become the basis of the new science of genetics that is so important to plant and animal breeders.

In 1953, Dr. James D. Watson and Dr. Francis Crick discovered how the laws of genetics worked with their amazing model of DNA, deoxyribonucleic acid, the molecule of heredity. DNA forms chromosomes in the nucleus of a cell, and a gene is one small section of the DNA that holds the code for a particular trait. Some traits require the action of several genes before they can be seen in the organism. A plant nucleus contains many chromosomes, and each one may hold more than 1,000 different genes.

Mendel's generations of peas had shown that inherited characteristics are logical and predictable. And even after Watson and Crick's discovery revealed the way these genetic blueprints are duplicated in each cell, genes were still generally thought of as simple units laid out in a fixed, linear sequence like a string of beads. It seemed unreasonable to think that any part of a gene could move from one site to another, or from cell to cell. Yet no one could really explain the sudden appearance of a new variety. Could the genes move around? While other researchers concentrated on the new technology of molecular genetics in the labs, Dr. Barbara McClintock found "jumping genes" in the cornfields.

Corn genetics is hard work. Like Gregor Mendel, the scientist must be out in the fields from cool dawn through the heat of the afternoon, watering young plants, tagging them, and meticulously moving pollen from tassel to flower to prevent a chance pollination. Dr. McClintock began her study of corn genetics as a botany major at Cornell University in the 1920s. She had wanted to study plant breeding, but that department did not admit women then. But after she earned her doctorate in botany, she found that women were not allowed to hold tenured professorships. So she moved her research to the Cold Spring Harbor laboratory on Long Island, where she watched a small patch of maize (Indian corn) grow for more than fifty years.

Through careful and tedious comparisons, Dr. McClintock found that some genes not only move to different locations on the chromosome, but these "jumping genes" can also leap from cell to cell and change the way traits are expressed in a plant. "They thought I was quite mad," Dr. McClintock said after she was awarded the Nobel Prize in Medicine and Physiology in 1983. A Nobel Prize committee spokesman called her work "one of the two greatest discoveries of our time in genetics."

In 1904, years before Dr. McClintock's research began, George Harrison Shull joined the Station for Experimental Evolution at Cold Spring Harbor. His first assignment was to plant display plots of corn to show visitors how Mendel's laws of inheritance work. And while he was working with the corn, Shull discovered how to inbreed and produce purebred lines. An inbred plant is one that fertilizes itself; the female flowers are fertilized by pollen from a male flower of the same plant. A purebred is a plant whose genes have become practically uniform from the extensive inbreeding.

With Edward M. East at the Connecticut Agricultural Experimental Station, Shull found that when they crossed two different inbred or pure lines of corn, they got a hybrid that was bigger and larger and had a higher yield than either of the parents. This result became known as *hybrid vigor*. Since 1930, new strains of hybrid corn have been developed that have raised the average yield from twenty-two bushels per acre to ninety-five bushels. Imagine what a difference that makes to a farmer's income.

Hybrid corn touched off a revolution in agricultural genetics, and researchers enthusiastically began to design crops with higher yields. A combination of the new hybrid varieties and improved farming techniques, such as irrigation and the use of better fertilizers and pesticides, brought about what has been called the Green Revolution. Crop yields have doubled and tripled. Countries

Dr. Barbara McClintock was honored in 1983 with a Nobel Prize for her discovery of "jumping genes."

such as India and Mexico that once had to import food now became self-sufficient and in some cases even began to export surplus food. Along with corn, the yields of the remaining "big four"—wheat, rice, and potatoes—whose annual production is equal to all other crops grown, increased dramatically.

In 1943 when Mexico was importing half the wheat needed to feed its people, the Mexican government asked for more help. The Rockefeller Foundation and the Mexican Ministry of Agriculture created a cooperative program to improve Mexico's crops, especially the wheat. Norman Borlaug, a plant pathologist from Iowa, was a member of the research team. He experimented with selections and crosses of wheat for ten years. By combining the germplasm of wheat from the United States, South America, Australia, and New Zealand, Borlaug produced a variety of wheat with a high yield and a resistance to many diseases, especially the stem rust so common in hot, wet Mexican summers.

About the same time, in 1953, Dr. Orville Vogel in Pullman, Washington, sent Borlaug some germplasm that contained genes for dwarf wheat, which had been discovered in Japan in 1946. Borlaug and his team crossed their high-yield, rust-resistant wheat with the Japanese dwarf variety. After thousands of offspring, only three were found to have all the desirable traits, and these were called "super wheat." The short wheat was "super" for that environment because ordinary tall wheat is easily knocked over by the wind and heavy rains and cannot be harvested.

Mexico became self-sufficient by 1963. Ninety-five percent of the wheat raised there was Borlaug's dwarf super wheat. India, Pakistan, Turkey, Egypt, Brazil, and many other countries quickly planted the super wheat, too. In the next ten years India's wheat production doubled. Enough was available to feed the nation without buying wheat from other countries. For more than 100 million people, Borlaug's new wheat made the difference between life and death. To honor this accomplishment, Norman Borlaug was awarded the Nobel Prize in 1970.

If super wheat could be bred, experts were sure that with enough time, money, and scientists, a super rice could also be produced. In 1960, the International Rice Research Institute was formed in the Philippines, and six years later it announced the new rice. This cross between an Indonesian variety and one from Taiwan became known as the miracle rice. The value of this crop in Asia increased by more than a billion dollars in just two years.

Germplasm from all over the world has been collected and incorporated into the plants we raise now. A plant breeder never knows when or where in some inaccessible region a valuable new species or variety will be found.

Six hundred miles off the coast of Ecuador on the Galapagos Islands, there is a wild tomato with a bitter, inedible fruit, but it can

Mary Lyons, a graduate student in seed and vegetable science at Cornell University, inspects snap bean varieties for resistance to mold.

45

survive on sand dunes washed by the salty spray from the Pacific Ocean. Breeders from the University of California at Davis have bred those genes for salt-water tolerance into tomato plants with edible fruit. The result is that the new tomato can be grown where only salt water is available for irrigation.

None of these new breeds appear quickly. It may take many years of breeding from the time a new species is discovered until it is ready for the farmer. When Hugh H. Iltis was on a collecting expedition in the Peruvian Andes in 1962, he found a yellow-flowered, sticky-leaved, scrawny-looking tomato. But he took about two dozen of the green and white fruit, which were smaller than cherries, and smashed them between paper to obtain and dry the seeds. Dr. Iltis mailed the dry seeds to Charles Rick, a tomato geneticist at the University of California. Twenty-four years later, Dr. Rick announced a new variety, a superior tomato for the canning industry. What took so long? Dr. Rick spent fourteen years comparing the scrawny Peruvian tomato with known tomatoes in order to identify it as a new species and then crossbreeding it with a commercial variety. It took another ten years before the new purebred variety was available to farmers. Plant breeding is not a job for the impatient.

Rafael Guzman was a young botany student at the University of Guadalajara in Mexico in 1977 when he made a discovery that has been called one of the greatest botanical finds of the century. Dr. Hugh Iltis sent Guzman a Christmas card that year, and on it was a drawing of an ancient ancestor of corn called *Zea diploperennis*. Botanists believed the plant had become extinct, but the card gave Guzman an idea. He took the picture with him on a hike into the foothills of the mountains near Guadalajara, where he asked local farmers whether they'd ever seen a similar plant. One farmer recognized the wild corn and led Guzman to a clearing, where they saw a thicket of tangled golden corn stalks eight feet tall, each bearing tiny seed husks filled with eight to ten brown kernels. Guzman dug up a plant and took it back to the university greenhouse, where he made a positive identification.

It was the ancient maize known to the Mexicans as teosinte, the fourth known species of wild corn. Not long after the discovery, Dr. Iltis joined Guzman on an expedition in that same region, hoping to find more of the teosinte. When they walked into a valley of overgrown pasture and clumps of trees, they saw growing all over the hillside teosinte, the *Zea diploperennis* they referred to as Z-dip. Iltis commented later in a news interview, "No botantist had ever been here before. Can you imagine how we felt? We just stared at each other in disbelief."

The excitement among plant breeders over the discovery of Z-dip had to do with the genetic properties of the ancient corn. It is a perennial, which means it grows back each year without replanting. Each stalk grows multiple ears of corn, unlike the single-eared corn of the United States grain belt. It is resistant to more than half a dozen plant diseases, and it is mountain tough; it grows in poor soil at high altitudes. If even the perennial genes from Z-dip could be bred into the germplasm of domestic corn, it would save billions of dollars for farmers, who would no longer have to replant each spring.

Z-dip is no longer in danger of extinction because it seeds are in seed banks all over the world. But it must still be maintained in the wild, where it can continually develop its natural resistance to new insects and diseases. A laboratory now stands on the site of that cornfield in the overgrown pasture of Mexico, and Dr. Rafael Guzman continues his research with Dr. Iltis at the University of Wisconsin.

The plant breeders who capture the best traits of wild species are almost making miracles, but they need the help of the plant savers.

5

Extinction

Almost any day somewhere in the rain forests of South or Central America you might see a man climb down from an enormous bulldozer, pick up a can of kerosene, pour it on a towering pile of tree limbs and stumps, and light it. And that could be the third or fourth pile of brush he'd burned that day after loggers had taken the best trees to sell for lumber. In the final clearing, the bulldozer scrapes clean all growth on the forest floor to a thin layer of top soil that will be planted with pasture grass for beef cattle. And this is only one of the ways in which the world's rain forests are being destroyed at the rate of fifty to a hundred acres *per minute*.

The beef raised on these cleared rain forests is too lean for the North American markets, where people enjoy fatter cuts for roasts and steaks. So it is ground up with fat from cattle raised in the United States and sold to the fast-food restaurants. This practice has been called the "hamburger connection," and it is responsible for turning nearly 40 percent of Central America's forest cover into pasture, with 90 percent of the cattle raised going to the United States and Canada.

In a broad band around the equator, the rain forests cover three million square miles, mostly in Third World countries. Only twenty years ago the rain forests were believed to be so vast that nothing could seriously damage them. But the need for building lumber, fuel, and food for the increasing populations of these countries has put the rain forests in jeopardy. And the use of two pieces of equipment—the lightweight chain saw and the bulldozer—has made the destruction fast, cheap, and relatively easy.

What is so unique and important about tropical rain forests? Although they make up only 6 to 7 percent of the earth's land mass, they contain 40 to 50 percent of the world's species of plants and animals. The small nation of Panama has as many species of living things as the entire continent of Europe! In one quarter of an acre in the Australian rain forest, you might find a hundred different species of trees, while you'd find ten species in two acres of New England forest.

The temperate forests of the United States and Canada are noted for their distinct plant neighborhoods. On a ridge you can find a beech and maple forest or an oak forest, while in a ravine there may be hemlocks, and along a stream willows will grow. There are relatively few species of plants but large numbers of each species grouped together.

In a tropical rain forest, however, there is a wide dispersal of species. There may be a single fern tree two dozen feet tall and not another like it for several hundreds of yards. But between those two fern trees may grow one or two of each of a hundred different species. There might be a spongy-barked tree with oval leaves, then a smooth-barked tree with long, vicious-looking thorns on its trunk. And nearby could be the "killer tree," called the strangler fig, which starts as a slender vine growing around another tree but matures into a great twisted, free-standing tree after killing the host tree that gave it its start.

Above, the branches of the trees in the rain forest are filled with

This 1935 print shows men clearing Brazilian forests for a coffee plantation.

plant life. Orchids, ferns, mosses, and other epiphytes grow along each branch and fill each crevice.

Another unusual group of plants of the tropics consists of the aroids, which grow among the tops of the tallest trees in the canopy of the rain forests. Aroids send down great bands of thick roots into the soil to absorb nutrients. These roots are the strong, flexible vines seen in the movies as Tarzan swings from tree to tree. In reality, the vines are used by some Indians to tie together the beams of their houses.

In the rain forest, every niche is filled. Life overlaps to form layer upon layer of different species. In the central region of the great Amazon basin, biologists counted more than 1,600 species of plants in an area 19 feet by 100 feet, which is less than half the size of an average house lot.

With intense competition for space, water, light, and nutrients, these plants have evolved all kinds of adaptations for survival, including ways to survive attack by the millions of pests, fungi, and bacteria that can destroy them. The tropical rain forest is a "hothouse" where some of the earth's oldest and most extensive germplasm thrives. So far this worldwide tropical hothouse has supplied us with pineapples, tapioca, cocoa (chocolate), and products from the rubber tree. It has given us drugs such as tranquilizers, antibiotics, and anticancer medicines.

A Brazilian chemist who specializes in tropical plants estimates that only 10 percent of the species in the Amazon have been analyzed, and other experts say that only one in six of all the species in the rain forest of the world has even been identified. Nobody really knows what's there or what can be done with it. But even plants with no immediate or obvious use may contain unique and useful genes. Genetic engineers can rearrange existing genes, but they cannot make new ones. Once a gene is lost, it is gone forever.

Rain forests have been reduced to less than half their original area. Half of the rich Amazon basin that stretches across Brazil is being destroyed at the rate of 5,000 square miles each year. That's an area the size of Connecticut. Colombia is losing about 253 square miles each year, and Venezuela has lost more than 6,500 square miles both to cattle grazing and farming.

But the destruction of the rain forests happens not in Third World countries alone. Three-fourths of Australia's forests have been cleared for sugarcane plantations and cattle ranches. The majestic red cedar trees, once prized for fine cabinetmaking, are almost extinct. Australian ranchers have a saying, "Cows can't eat cedar," and now cattle graze where the red cedar once grew. Nearly two-thirds of Australia's tropical plants can't be found anywhere else on earth, and with the loss of those plants, their germplasm is lost, too.

Ninety-nine percent of the flowering plants in Hawaii are unique to those islands; they grow nowhere else. But of the 3,000 species once found in those lush forests, 270 are extinct and 800 are in danger. Since the arrival in Hawaii of Americans and Europeans 200 years ago, two-thirds of the rain forests there have been destroyed for cities and plantations. Many of the trees were ground into chips and sold to the electric company for fuel.

A rain forest is a fragile ecosystem. Its rich vegetation disguises poor soil. In the temperate forests, the life-supporting nutrients are held locked into the soil by slowly decaying organic material. But in the tropics, the nutrients are locked in the trees and other plants. In the moist heat, dead vegetation quickly decays, and the nutrients are immediately recycled into living plants. What does enter the loose, porous soil quickly leaches away into streams.

When rain forests are bulldozed down, what's left is nutrient-poor soil that can't support a farm crop for more than a few years. Then the landowners turn those acres into pasture for cattle because grasses don't require rich nutrients. But not all the land clearing is done by large corporations that buy and bulldoze huge tracts of land. Some of the clearing is more gradual. In the Amazon

53

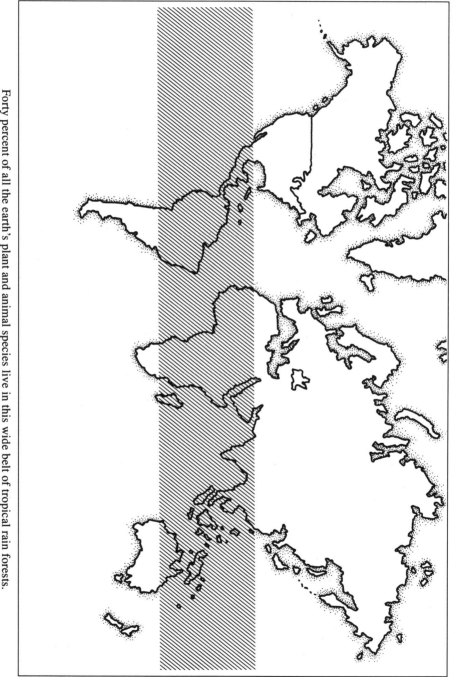

Forty percent of all the earth's plant and animal species live in this wide belt of tropical rain forests.

basin, farm families are moving out into the rain forest, looking for cheap land bordering newly built roads. Often these families have been promised free land, seed, and easy credit by lumber companies that no longer need the land or by governments that are trying to find room for growing populations. A family may cut and burn a couple of acres of the forest to plant rice and maize. But in a few years, when the soil has run out of nutrients and the crops fail, the family moves farther into the forest. The land they leave behind is taken over by ranchers to add to their cattle pasturage.

The rain forests are essentially a nonrenewable resource. Even if left alone after being bulldozed, it would take several hundreds of years, if not thousands, for the land to return to its original state, and most of the original species would never be seen again. Many biologists agree that we have entered a period of extinction of

Where settlers move further into the forests of western Brazil, they cut and burn lush forests. Soon the thin topsoil erodes into a wasteland.

species second only to the Cretaceous Period 65 million years ago, when the dinosaurs and many other species disappeared.

But we're losing germplasm not just in the rain forests. Other ecosystems are in danger, too. Swamps and salt marshes are being drained to make room for hotels and condominiums with an ocean view. A salt marsh is a unique ecosystem containing plants called halophytes. If the salt-survival genes of the halophytes can be combined into food crops, we could have crops that could be irrigated with seawater. Researchers at a University of Arizona field station in Mexico are raising a halophyte crop that will be used to feed cattle. If the project is successful, it could mean that halophyte crops might be raised on the 20,000 miles of barren lands along unused desert coastlines, and a billion people fed. If saltwater marshes are destroyed, the germplasm of many useful halophytes will become extinct.

The desert is another fragile ecosystem, easily destroyed. In many deserts the grains of sand are held together by lichen and soil fungi. It's not a firm surface, and it's all too quickly destroyed by recreational vehicles. Once the surface is broken, the winds and rain erode the sand and kill the vegetation. Dune buggies, dirt bikes, and all-terrain vehicles are ruining the deserts of the Southwest states. More than a hundred species of plants in California's deserts are now on the endangered list, and among them may be plants that could yield industrial chemicals or medicines. Some useful ones have already been discovered. A scrubby little bush called the jojoba is responsible for saving the sperm whale because the jojoba bean produces an oil that can replace sperm oil as an industrial lubricant. Another desert shrub, the guayule, produces rubber similar to that from cultivated rubber trees that require moist tropical soil.

All these different ecosystems contain the world's data bank of germplasm, and once they are gone, so is that deposit of irreplaceable genes.

The Green Revolution was successful because it gave high-yield hybrid crops to many areas of the world. But the unfortunate side of that revolution came when farmers stopped raising the old varieties of plants. Those seeds died out, and the genes were lost. And then the farmers found that some of the new hybrids were not as well suited to the Third World conditions as they'd hoped. They weren't as resistant to some local pests and diseases as the old crops had been, and the new hybrids needed expensive fertilizer and more cultivation to produce large crops. In some famine-stricken nations, farmers were reduced to eating the seeds they'd saved for the next year's planting. But the old germplasm was gone.

So what's being done about it?

6

The Bankers and Savers

The plain-looking building at the edge of the campus of the University of Colorado in Fort Collins holds one of the world's most valuable collections. Ultimately more important than a bank or museum or library, it is the National Seed Storage Laboratory, part of the National Plant Germplasm System. Built in 1958, this seed bank stores more than 250,000 samples from wild and domestic crops in all parts of the planet. In dark, refrigerated rooms, row upon row of shelves hold row upon row of trays of seeds in small carefully marked sacks. It is only one of several seed banks in the United States and other parts of the world where germplasm of primitive cultivated varieties, their weed cousins, and modern varieties are stored. Some samples are from rare, endangered species, and others are already extinct in their natural habitats.

Although this kind of seed or gene banking is relatively new, the earth's soil has been storing plant genes for centuries. In dry or cold soil, seeds can remain alive for years. The colder the climate, the better the chance a seed has for survival. In the frozen Arctic soil, someone found the seeds of lupine, a popular flower in modern

Thousands of seed samples are stored in metal cans under controlled temperature and humidity at the National Seed Storage Laboratory.

gardens. Even though the seeds were shown by radiocarbon dating to be 10,000 years old, some of them still grew when they were planted.

When seeds arrive at a seed bank, they are dried and then designated for either long-term, medium, or short-term storage. At temperatures between -10° and -20° Celsius (14° to -4° F), seeds can last about a hundred years. If seeds are expected to be stored for twenty years, they are kept at temperatures ranging from 0° to 5° C (32° to 41° F). For storage up to five years, seeds can be kept at room temperature. At the seed bank some seeds will be constantly removed for evaluation of traits by breeders and genetic engineers; these seeds are kept in medium and short-term storage. The long-term collection is rarely disturbed, and usually duplicates of those seeds are sent to another seed bank as a backup in case the original collection is accidently destroyed.

To be useful, a seed bank must have information that is easily retrieved. Records are kept not only about the seeds' characteristics but also about the environment the stock came from. In many cases, little is known about the sample's disease or pest resistance, its tolerance to cold or drought, or other hidden traits. Charles Murphy, who is acting director of the National Plant Germplasm System, says that 85 percent of the stored seeds have not been evaluated in this way. The system is like a library that catalogs only the title and author of a book, but nothing about its contents. A lot more time and money must be spent on the data system before anyone can know the real potential of the stored germplasm.

In addition to the seed bank at Fort Collins, Colorado, the National Plant Germplasm System has a Germplasm Resources Laboratory in Beltsville, Maryland; three Plant Introduction Stations in Maryland, Georgia, and Florida; four state/federal regional stations in Washington, Iowa, New York, and Georgia; a potato station in Wisconsin; and eight clonal laboratories scattered throughout the United States. Included in the system is a large group of labs and banks in state and private universities and botanical gardens.

Our large national germplasm banking system is part of a worldwide system of forty-three major gene banks organized by the United Nations to collect and store germplasm accessible to all nations. Although Russia, with the second largest collection after the United States, is not part of the UN system, their plant scientists exchange germplasm and cooperate with other scientists freely.

Each germplasm bank usually specializes in a single crop or in the modern and ancient varieties of that region. For example, at the International Rice Research Institute in the Philippines, 60,000 rice varieties have been stored since 1960. Germplasm from its collection was the basis of the super rice developed in 1966.

The International Potato Center in Lima, Peru, has the world's largest collection of potatoes, with more than 13,000 samples. The

This scientist at the National Seed Storage Laboratory in Colorado is checking the seedlings grown from stored seeds.

Vavilov Institute in Russia has the second largest collection, with the Potato Station in Wisconsin third with 2,800 samples of more than ninety species.

The Ismir Center in Turkey specializes in wheat, barley, alfalfa, and other grains collected from southern Europe and northern Africa, with 2,500 varieties from Turkey alone. The Iberian Gene Bank in Madrid, Spain, stores plant specimens from all regions surrounding the Mediterranean Sea.

Many of the germplasm banks in the tropics have no deep freeze storage facilities, and periodically the seeds from those collections must be planted and raised to revitalize another generation of seeds for storage. Rice collections at the International Rice Research Institute in the Philippines are "grown out" in the same manner every ten to fifteen years. Scandinavian scientists don't have that problem. They have found a natural freezer deep inside an Arctic mountain on the island of Longyearbyen, where 4,000 different crop seeds are protected from everything, including nuclear disaster.

Not all crops can be stored as seeds because some seeds are too large or pulpy. Some don't "breed true," which means that ten seeds from one plant may produce ten completely different offspring. Fruit, berry, and root crops such as potatoes cannot be stored as seed. Instead they are stored as clones, exact genetic copies of the original mother plants, which can be grown from a bud or a piece of root or stem into a whole plant. Each of the eight clonal labs and storage centers in the United States specializes in a specific group of plants. Grapes, walnuts, prunes, and olives are stored at Davis, California. Avocados, bananas, and coffee are stored in Miami, Florida. Citrus crops are kept at both the Riverside and Orlando, California, labs, and apples and grapes are saved at Geneva, New York.

Keeping clones is much different and more expensive than keeping seeds, which are nice, compact dormant embryos. In a field or greenhouse, each clone must be grown by budding or grafting it to rootstock, or by rooting stem cuttings, or by some other method of asexual propagation.

At the seven-hundred-acre New York State Agricultural Experiment Station in Geneva, New York, the United States clonal lab stores apples and "cold hardy" grapes, which are those that can stand cold winters. (Warm-weather grapes are kept in California.) This station, operated by Cornell University, was started in 1887, and the clonal bank, run by the federal government, was added in 1984. Since then it has put together the largest apple collection in the country with 2,500 types.

The first job of the apple repository was to find and store all the varieties in the United States, especially those in danger of being lost. Through a network of growers and nurserymen, scientists at the Geneva station heard about an apple grower in South Dakota who was retiring and selling out to a land developer. They were able to collect samples of his large collection of unique varieties just before the bulldozers arrived to wipe them out.

When apple samples arrive at the Geneva station, they are just short lengths of new growth cut from branches of the apple tree. These are called scions. Five buds from each scion are grafted onto each apple seedling growing in six-inch clay pots. These seedlings are then put into a thermal therapy chamber for three weeks at a temperature of 36° C (97° F) to allow the buds to "outgrow" any viruses they might harbor. The virus-free buds are then grafted onto both dwarf and standard size tree seedlings in a temporary holding field, where they will grow for two years. Any found to contain viruses are removed, and the others are ready for the long-term storage fields. At this stage, the scions are grafted on two standard tree seedlings in one field, and onto one dwarf seedling in another field as a backup.

Dr. Philip Forsline, curator of the Geneva Clonal Repository, said that from their 1988 collection, 1,500 specimens were sent to

A rootstock developing scion

scientists, nurserymen, and other growers, making both old and new apple germplasm available to the world.

Many botanical gardens were collecting and raising plants long before anyone worried about plant extinction, and they have become an unexpected bank of exotic species. One survey showed that 34 percent of the 1,878 endangered plants in Europe were found growing in botanical gardens. The Royal Botanical Gardens at Kew, England, is one of the oldest and largest, with 47,000 growing species in its collection. One of the rarest is *Sophora toromiro*, the only surviving tree species from Easter Island in the Pacific Ocean. By 1962, there was not a single tree left on Easter Island; all were extinct, except for the single plant at Kew.

At Harvard University's Arnold Arboretum, the Center for Plant Conservation is attempting to collect and preserve every endangered plant in the United States, with the help of eighteen other botanical gardens.

But not all plant collectors are professionals. There is a growing number of hobbyists, home gardeners, and semiprofessionals determined to save the "heirloom" plants. These are the plants our forefathers brought from their homelands when they came to North America. Seeds from these immigrant plants are our land races, and they contain genes not found in the hybrids we buy from ordinary seed companies. The garden-variety plant savers are keeping alive such specimens as Jacob's Cattle beans, Howling Mob corn, and Silver Bell squash—names not found in the usual seed catalog.

Seed exchanges have been organized to make heirloom varieties easily available. One of the largest is the Seed Savers Exchange started by Kent and Diane Whealy in Iowa in 1975. They now have more than 600 members who offer 5,000 rare vegetable seeds. Others are the Abundant Life Seed Foundation in Washington, the Heirloom Garden Seeds in California, and the Plant Finders of America in Kentucky.

Some savers specialize. The Driskills of Alberta, Canada,

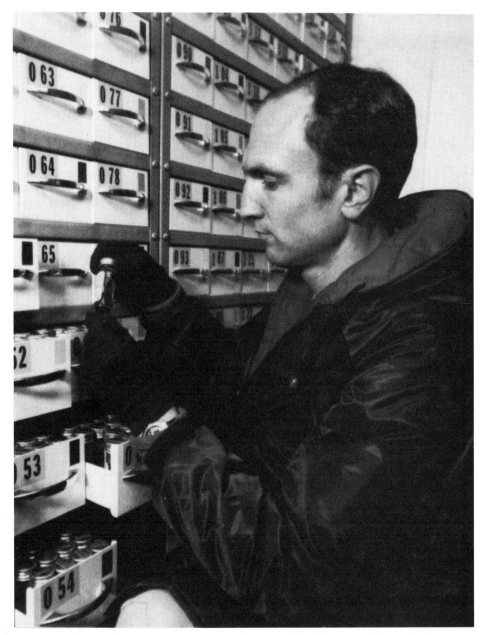

At Kew Gardens in England seed samples are kept in cold storage where scientists can use them for research.

collect and exchange only cold-tolerant plants. They began corresponding with other northern farmers looking for crops that would tolerate the cold and ripen in the short growing season, and they found so much interest in the project that they started the seed exchange in 1983. Their catalog, called Siberia Seeds, lists plants named Glacier, Subarctic Maxi, and a recent tomato called Landry's Russian.

The gardens of early settlers in the new world bloomed with cherished flowers grown from seeds packed carefully for the long ocean voyage to America. Harrison's Yellow rose was a favorite around the dooryards of farms all over New England, and as pioneers and gold prospectors moved west, they carried with them the roots of these roses to plant around their new settlements. Those yellow roses still bloom in ghost towns of the West. They're often called "cellar" roses because they are found around the foundations of long-abandoned farmhouses. Descendants of other early immigrant flowers thrive in old cemeteries, where they were planted around stones more than a hundred years ago. Many old-fashioned roses grown before 1967 are cultivated today and sold through catalogs like Lowe's Own Root Roses in New Hampshire.

The germplasm goes on because of these dedicated savers, and young people are lending a hand. In the summer of 1989, forty-seven teams of high school volunteers from the Student Conservation Association worked in wilderness areas from New Hampshire to California. Thirty-five of those teams went to Yellowstone National Park to collect seeds of the lodgepole pines and help replant forests destroyed by the fires of 1988. Other teams cleared trails and did extensive revegetation work in Olympic National Park in western Washington, and still others helped spray the aphids that infested Fraser firs in the Great Smoky Mountains National Park in North Carolina and Tennessee. For more information about this nonprofit volunteer organization, you can write to the Student Conservation Association, Inc., P.O. Box 550, Charlestown, New Hampshire 03603.

Four thousand kids from kindergarten to sixth grade collected seeds in a program at the Cornell Plantation in Ithaca, New York, called LEAP (Learning About Plants), funded by a National Science Foundation grant. These are not the only programs, of course. All over the United States and Canada, young people are learning how they can help save our great resource of germplasm.

7

Green Medicine

When those fifteenth century Spanish explorers returned from Peru, they had a hard time convincing people to eat the new vegetable called the potato. As far as anyone knew, the potato was poisonous. Wasn't it a close cousin to the deadly nightshade? Everyone knew that a single berry from the deadly nightshade (*Atropa belladonna*) was enough to kill a person. And another potato cousin, an herb called henbane, was used to make "knockout drops."

Jimsonweed, which is also in the potato family, didn't have such a great reputation either. A sip of its juice or a few of the seeds could be fatal. Even now, farmers try to keep their pastures clear of jimsonweed so cattle and horses won't graze on it and die. Jimsonweed probably originated in India, but it became well known when it came to America for the first time at the new colonial port of Jamestown, Virginia, early in the 1600s. Botanists think the jimsonweed may have been mixed with other foods and mistaken for spinach, which caused the sailors who ate it to become violently ill. At first the plant was called Jamestown weed, but over the years its name changed to jimsonweed.

Many medicines are made from these potato cousins. Atropine, which doctors use to open the pupils of the eyes in bright light during examination, comes from jimsonweed. It is also used in medicines that increase the heartbeat, or dry up a runny nose, or ease the wheezing of hayfever. The "truth serum" scopolamine, made from nightshade and henbane, is also used in small amounts to counteract seasickness.

Plants have always been the basis of medicine and drugs. It's likely that the earliest cave dwellers bound up their wounds with leaves and learned what plants helped heal and soothe fevers. Today, 80 percent of the world's people use medicines made mainly from plants, and almost half the prescription drugs in the United States contain natural substances from plants.

But imagine how difficult it must have been to find the right dose, one that would heal instead of kill. Today, we have a medicine called ergotamine made from a deadly fungus known as ergot. It alleviates migraine headaches and eases childbirth pain, but between the years 1580 and 1900, there were sixty-five major epidemics of ergot poisoning in Europe.

The poisonous ergot fungus grows on rye. Even a few kernels of rye blighted by this fungus, baked into bread, and eaten was enough to cause wild hallucinations and madness. People thought it was the work of the devil. In 1096, the Order of the Hospital Brothers of St. Anthony was founded to care for the ill and dying. Ergot poisoning became known as St. Anthony's fire because the victims' fingers and toes turned black and fell off as though charred by fire. When Peter the Great of Russia was preparing an invasion of Turkey in 1722, more than 20,000 of his soldiers became ill or died from eating ergot-contaminated bread. The invasion was called off. And yet, over the years people learned to use the ergot for healing instead of harm.

Malaria has probably killed more people than all the wars and plagues combined. In 1938, for example, there were more than 300,000 reported cases of malaria, with 20,000 in just one province of Brazil alone. Early in the 1600s, Jesuit missionaries living with the Peruvian Indians were amazed to find that the Indians knew how to treat malaria with medicine made from the "fever bark trees" that grow on the eastern slopes of the Andes Mountains. The active ingredient in the bark of these chinchona trees was quinine, which is still used to treat malaria and other diseases.

The list goes on. Mexican yams gave us the raw materials for the first steroids; foxglove gave us digitalis used to treat heart diseases; and the periwinkle provided the chemicals vinblastine and vincristine that lower the white blood cell count. Before these periwinkle drugs, 89 percent of children stricken with leukemia died. With the drugs, more than 80 percent live.

The most commonly used medicine, an ordinary aspirin, came from the bark of the willow tree. Greek physicians treated pain with extracts of the bark 2,400 years ago. Salicylic acid in the willow bark is the active ingredient, and in large doses it can cause intestinal upset. But in 1899, German chemists made it into a safe compound called acetylsalicylic acid, or aspirin.

Pharmaceutical companies are always on the lookout for new drug sources. Penicillin was found in a soil sample, and so was an amazing new drug that keeps a body from rejecting transplanted organs. A microbiologist at the Sandoz Corporation found an unknown fungus in a soil sample he collected in Norway, but he was disappointed when the protein he took from that fungus didn't seem to fight infection. He called it cyclosporine and put it on a shelf out of sight and almost out of mind. But the chief of immunology at Sandoz kept going back to study the protein, thinking it must be good for something. And was it ever! Before cyclosporine, a patient's own immune system would reject a transplanted organ, such as a heart or kidney, as a foreign invader. Today thousands of transplants are successful because cyclosporine keeps the patient's own white blood cells from attacking a surgically implanted new organ.

American Indians treated headaches and fevers with medicines from the bark of
the willow tree.

In 1988 a new medicine was found in an old tree called the ginkgo. Naturalist Charles Darwin called the ginkgo a living fossil because its ancestors grew 300 million years ago. Dinosaurs probably nibbled on its leaves. For the last 5,000 years, the Chinese people have used extracts of the ginkgo's leaves to treat heart and lung ailments as well as coughs, asthma, and some allergies. Now chemists at Harvard University have made a compound they call ginkgolide B, which they think will be widely used to treat asthma, various circulatory problems, and Alzheimer's disease. Medicinal products from the ginkgo tree are used widely in Asia and Europe, but they have not yet been approved for use in the United States or Britain.

Scientists who specialize in ethnobotany, the study of tribal people's use of plants, are stepping up their search for new sources

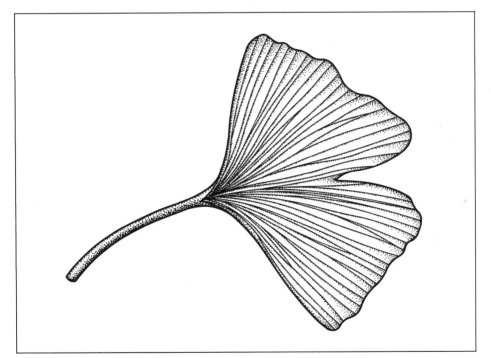

The bark and leaves of the ginkgo tree have been used for centuries in China to treat heart and lung diseases.

of medical and agricultural products. Research teams sponsored by The World Wildlife Fund are going from village to village in Africa, South America, and Asia asking people and their medicine men how they treat various diseases. The National Cancer Institute awarded a $2.5 million contract to the New York Botanical Garden and the University of Illinois teams to collect and test tropical plants that might be used in the treatment of cancer.

Fewer than 5 percent of the quarter of a million plant species on earth have been tested as a source of potential medicines. There may be plants growing somewhere that not only cure cancer but perhaps the common cold. Each species of plant has adapted to the stress of changes in its environment and developed its own defense system against pests and disease. They have stored these systems and adaptations in the genes of their germplasm. Some of these stored defense systems can work for us, too, if only we can find these plants before they are destroyed and lost forever.

8

The Green Gene Revolution

Each year on ten acres of land at the International Potato Center in Peru, workers cultivate 6,000 potato plants, collect the tubers, store them, and plant them again the following year. But with a technique called tissue culture, a few technicians can raise 6,000 potato clones in test tubes in one small laboratory.

In human terms, tissue culture is like growing carbon copies of a person from a small piece of that person's skin. In plant tissue culture, scientists cut the tip of a growing root, put it in a test tube with a mixture of minerals and growth hormones, and store it under neon lights at temperatures between 6° and 10° C (43° and 50° F). Every two years fresh cuttings are taken from these new plants and recultured. In the near future, scientists expect to be able to freeze and store tissue cultures in liquid nitrogen, which will eliminate the need for new cultures.

Tissue culture won't replace the seed banks, but it will make possible cheaper, better methods of preserving plants. Most germplasm, especially grains, will still be stored as seed. But the fleshier plants, such as berries, nuts, bananas, coffee, and potatoes, can be stored more efficiently as cultured tissue. As an added

Thousands of plants can be grown in tissue culture in a room such as this, where a technician is checking the results of one of the breeding experiments.

benefit, tissue cultured plants are virtually free of diseases, unlike plants grown in fields and greenhouses.

With the present biotechnology of tissue and cell culture, new generations of plants can be bred in days or weeks instead of years, and a few test tubes or culture dishes can hold an amount of germplasm equivalent to many acres of field plants. A scientist can look at hundreds of millions of cells in one small container and easily evaluate plant traits. One biotechnician said that tissue culture collections are like pharmacies filled with unlabeled miracle drugs waiting to be analyzed for use as medicines, natural pesticides, and herbicides.

Experiments to find plants that are immune to disease or resistant to drought or cold can be quickly done in tissue culture. A fungus that causes blight, for example, can be introduced into a single culture dish containing millions of plant cells. If any of those cells are unaffected by the blight, they are removed and recultured into a small plant. That plant can then be raised in a greenhouse or field to see if the whole plant is resistant and if that trait is passed along to its offspring.

The prospects for producing new and hardier plants for food, pharmaceuticals, and energy through genetic engineering seem unlimited. No longer are breeders limited to combining genes of closely related plants. Now all genes are potential germplasm to be bred into crops. It may be possible to engineer tropical rubber, banana, pineapple, and warm-weather citrus fruits to withstand the colder temperatures and shorter growing season of Maine and Canada. All crops might be engineered to produce their own fertilizer, to be resistant to disease and pests, or to survive severe drought. It may be possible to make corn so sweet you could eat cornflakes without adding sugar, or to raise peach-size strawberries on bushes where they'd be easy to pick.

The two processes used to make these miracles are called protoplast fusion and recombinant DNA. One of the biggest problems to overcome in combining the germplasm of two plants is getting through the cell wall. Unlike an animal cell, which has no wall, the protective plant cell wall is unlikely to take in foreign germplasm. That problem was solved by removing the cell wall with chemicals called enzymes. What's left is called a protoplast, which is the living part of the cell containing the germplasm-packed nucleus, surrounded by liquid cytoplasm that contains all the cell structures.

Protoplasts from two different plants can be mixed together in a culture dish, and some of them will fuse, combining the genetic material of both. The protoplasts don't even have to be from closely related species, which is necessary in regular plant breeding. The mixed protoplasts are recultured in solutions of chemicals that stimulate growth, and the mass of new cells that grow is called a *callus*. Under proper conditions, the callus will become a new plant.

It may sound like a simple process, but it isn't. Only a small percent of protoplasts fuse and, of those, only a few will form a callus. And an even smaller number, if any, of the calluses will grow into a whole plant. When a new plant does grow, it may be a real surprise. In one experiment, a cabbage protoplast was combined with a radish protoplast, but it produced a totally inedible plant with cabbage roots and radish leaves. Carrot and parsley were fused in the hopes of getting a carrot root with a parsley top, and it worked—except the carrots were small and the parsley was scrawny. The protoplast fusion that combined the tomato and potato plants into a pomato was not successful commercially because both vegetables that resulted were small and poor in quality.

But sometimes it does work. A potato fused with a wild plant called the black nightshade, which is resistant to the herbicide triazine, resulted in a good quality potato that now contains the resistant genes, too. Herbicides sprayed on a field kill both weeds and crops. But weeds that compete with crops for water, minerals, and fertilizer cause major problem for farmers. They would

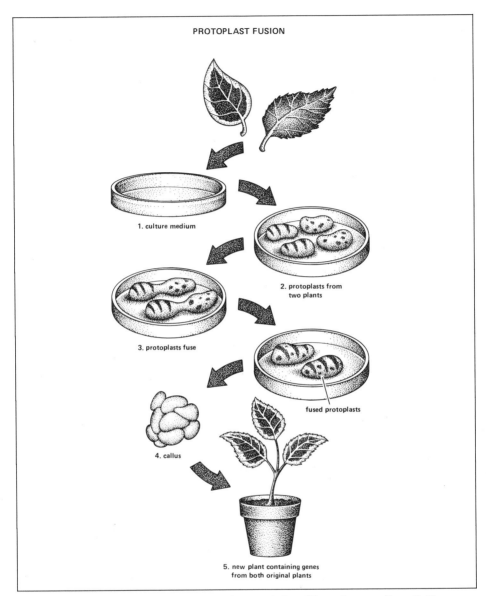

PROTOPLAST FUSION

1. culture medium

2. protoplasts from
   two plants

3. protoplasts fuse

fused protoplasts

4. callus

5. new plant containing genes
   from both original plants

1. Cells are taken from two dfferent plants and placed in a culture medium. **2.** The cell walls are chemically removed to form protoplasts. **3.** The different protoplasts fuse with each other to form a new genetic combination. **4.** One or more of the new protoplasts may grow and divide to form a clump of cells called a callus. **5.** The callus may then grow into a new plant containing the characteristics of both original plants.

welcome crops that could survive sprays that killed weeds only. For that reason, many large chemical companies are spending a lot of money on research to engineer crops that will be resistant to the herbicides they manufacture to kill weeds.

The second way of engineering new hybrids is called gene splicing or recombinant DNA. To move genetic material artificially in the lab, a genetic engineer takes a segment of DNA from the nucleus of one plant cell and transfers it to a segment of DNA from another plant cell, where the foreign DNA combines with the host DNA. That recombined cell is cultured in a nutrient solution and grows into a new plant that shows the traits of the foreign DNA. It's a technique that is more specific than protoplast fusion in which all the genes are mixed together, and it's easier to predict the outcome.

The two big problems in developing the recombination of genes were how to transfer the segment of DNA and how to get a new plant to grow from a single cell. In animals, the transfer of genes is done by inserting the genes into a harmless bacterium called *E. coli*. But most bacteria can't get through the cell wall of a plant, and those that can are harmful. So the genetic engineers tried the harmful bacteria.

They chose *Agrobacterium tumefaciens*, a bacterium that causes a cancerlike growth called crown gall disease in plants. The genes for this disease are located on a small closed loop of DNA known as a plasmid. They removed the DNA fragment that causes the gall tumor from the TI (tumor inducing) plasmid and replaced it with the foreign genes they wanted transferred into the plant cell.

One of the earliest gene splicing successes in plants occurred in 1981, when a gene from a bean plant was transferred into a sunflower cell, producing the "sunbean," which is still in the experimental stage.

In 1986, a gene from a virus was spliced into the TI plasmid and transferred to both tobacco and tomato cells. The resulting

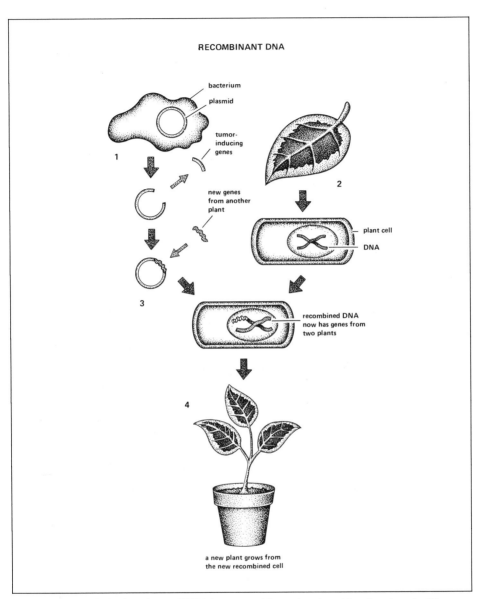

RECOMBINANT DNA

bacterium

plasmid

tumor-inducing genes

1

new genes from another plant

2

plant cell

DNA

3

recombined DNA now has genes from two plants

4

a new plant grows from the new recombined cell

1. Tumor-inducing piece of DNA is removed from the plasmid and replaced with a new piece of plant DNA containing specific traits the breeder wants to appear in the new plant. **2.** A single cell is removed from another plant. **3.** The bacteria plasmid carries the new genes into the plant cell where they combine with the DNA. **4.** The cell regenerates into a new plant containing the new genes and their characteristics.

plants were resistant to the tobacco mosaic virus disease, which is a major problem in agriculture. Genetic engineers hope to apply the technique to other important crops to make squash, potatoes, peppers, and other vegetables resistant to other viruses.

In one transfer, genes that produce pesticides were taken from bacteria and put into plants. Now when an insect takes a bite of that plant, it gets a mouthful of the poison and dies, although there's not enough of the pesticide in the plant to be toxic to animals, including man.

The TI plasmid transfer is a useful technique, but it doesn't work on corn, wheat, and rice. These crops, and other grains, must be altered by direct DNA transfer, and that's done by mixing foreign DNA fragments directly with protoplasts of the plants to be changed. The protoplasts take up the DNA and combine it with their own. The success rate for this kind of transfer was small until 1986, when Dr. Virginia Walbot and her team at Stanford University discovered that short, intense bursts of electricity passed through the culture would increase the number of cells that would take foreign DNA.

Another method of direct DNA transfer is done by microinjection with a "gene gun." Foreign DNA is injected under pressure directly into cell cytoplasm or nuclei with a microscopic needle. Because it is a complex process and only one cell at a time can be injected, it's not yet very efficient, but the research continues.

Whatever method is used to transfer the genes, there is still a major problem with regenerating the clump of cells, the callus, into a whole plant. Wheat, rice, and corn had resisted all attempts to grow from a callus until 1987 when scientists at the University of Nottingham, England, announced the successful regeneration of a rice plant from protoplasts. They had found the right temperature, amount of light, and mixture of hormones, minerals, and other growth-inducing chemicals. The same temperature and light are not right for all plants, nor does the same culture mixture work on all plants. Geneticists in search of the perfect culture trade recipes in the same way that cooks exchange cake recipes.

Biotechnology is not a substitute for conventional methods of plant breeding used by nurserymen and farmers, but it's certainly a powerful tool. Ordinary crossbreeding, selection, and final testing for new varieties can take more than ten years, but with the methods of biotechnology, the same thing can be accomplished in a year or two. If a new disease should suddenly infect a crop, genetic engineers might be able to produce a resistant variety of that crop quite quickly.

Scientists have great hopes for their new tools and methods. The legumes, such as peas, soybeans, peanuts, beans, and clover, harbor nitrogen-fixing bacteria in small lumps or nodules on their roots. The bacteria don't harm the plant; they help it by taking nitrogen from the air and putting it into the ground in a form the plant can use for fertilizer. In other words, legumes fertilize themselves with the help of bacteria. If bioengineers can find the genes in legumes responsible for this working partnership with bacteria, they may be able to splice those genes into corn, wheat, rice, and other major crops.

The Green Revolution produced crops with tremendous yields, but only when the crops were supplied with huge amounts of fertilizer, water, pesticides, and mineral-rich soil. The new hybrids increased the world's food supply, but many of them have proved unsuitable to agriculture in Third World nations. And it's these countries that so desperately need reliable crops to feed their fast-growing populations.

The Green Gene Revolution is part of the answer. Given enough time and money for research, it may produce high-yield, self-fertilizing, drought-tolerant, disease- and pest-resistant crops.

One-third of the corn crop and one-third of the soybeans in the United States were lost in the devastating drought of 1988. North

American summers seem to be getting hotter and winters milder. Scientists have been warning us about the "greenhouse effect," the depletion of the atmosphere's ozone layer, and the addition of pollutants to the air that are causing a gradual worldwide warming. While some regions will bake dry, others will become cooler and wetter. Farmers may need a whole new range of crops to survive earth's changing climate.

For all the new technology, neither the genetic engineer nor the conventional plant breeder can make new genes. They can only manipulate those found in nature. When a plant species or variety is gone, it cannot be brought back. The fragile ecosystems of coastal wetlands and tropical rain forests are warehouses of germplasm that must be preserved, along with the germplasm of primitive cultivated crops.

There can be no political boundaries when it comes to saving the earth's store of germplasm. The seeds for our survival on this planet of plant eaters are all here; we need only to find them and keep them safe for generations to come.

Further Reading

Beaty, John Y. *Luther Burbank Plant Magician*. New York: Julian Messner, 1943.

Dodge, Bertha S. *Plants that Changed the World*. Boston: Little, Brown and Co., 1959.

Doyle, Jack. *Altered Harvest*. New York: Penguin Books, 1985.

Edlin, H. L. *Plants and Man*. New York: Natural History Press, 1969.

Elkington, John. *The Gene Factory*. London: Century Publishing, 1985.

Healey, B. J. *The Plant Hunters*. New York: Charles Scribner's Sons, 1975.

Kew: Gardens for Science and Pleasure. Owings Mills, Maryland: Stemmer House Publishers, 1982.

Klein, Richard M. *The Green World*. New York: Harper and Row, 1979.

Koopowitz, Harold and Kaye, Hilary. *Plant Extinction*. Washington, D.C.: Stone Wall Press, 1983.

Magic and Medicine of Plants. Pleasantville, New York: Readers Digest Association, 1986.

Ricciuti, Edward R. *Plants in Danger.* New York: Harper and Row, 1979.

Schultes, Richard Evans. *Where the Gods Reign.* Arizona and London: Synergetic Press,1988.

Stone, Doris M. *The Lives of Plants.* New York: Charles Scribner's and Sons, 1983.

Wilson, Charles Morrow. *Green Treasures.* Philadelphia: Macrae Smith Co., 1974.

Witt, Steven C. Brief Book, *Biotechnology and Genetic Diversity.* San Francisco: California Agricultural Lands Project, 1985.

Index

grafts, 37, 40, 64
grape storage, 63-63
Green Revolution, 42, 57, 85
guayule (rubber plant), 17, 56
Guzman, Dr. Rafael, 46
gypsy moths, 18

H halophytes, 16, 56
Harvard University, 37, 66, 75
Harvard University Botanical Museum, 32
Hatshepsut, Queen of Egypt, 28
Hawaii, 53
henbane, 71-72
Hooker, William, 25-26
Horticultural Society of London, 25
hybrid vigor, 42

I Iberian Gene Bank, Madrid, 63
iguana, 18, 20
Iltis, Dr. Hugh H., 46-47
India, 44, 71
International Potato Center, 30, 62, 77
International Rice Institute, 45, 62-63
Ireland, 9, 11, 14
Irish potato famine, 9

Ismir Center, Turkey, 63

J Japan, 15, 44
Jesuit missionaries, 73
jimsonweed, 71-72
jojoba beans, 56
juglone, 16

K Karhan, Dr. Richard, 21
knockout drops, 71. *See* henbane
kudzu vine, 15

L land races, 30, 32
L.E.A.P. program (Learning About Plants), 69
Lenin All-Union Academy of Natural Sciences, 30
leukemia, 73
"lumper" potato, 11, 14

M malaria, 72
Massachusetts Institute of Technology, 32
McClintock, Dr. Barbara, 41-43
McDonald's restaurant, 38
Mendel, Gregor, 39, 41-42
Mexican Ministry of Agriculture, 44
Mexico, 32, 44, 46-47, 56
Meyers, Frank, 28-29
Murphy, Charles, 61

T tannins, 20
teosinte (ancient maize), 47
tepary beans, 32
thistle, 18, 19
tissue culture, 77-79
tomato, 46, 80
trees,
  balsam poplar, 16
  digger pine, 26
  Douglas fir, 24, 26
  ginkgo, 75
  ponderosa pine, 15, 26-27
  silver fir, 26
  Sitka willow, 21
  Sophora toromiro, 66.
   See Easter Island
  strangler fig ("killer
   tree"), 50
  sugar pine, 26
  walnut, 16
  western white pine, 26
  willow, 73-74
truth serum, 72. *See*
  scopolamine

U United States, 9, 12, 15,
   18, 28, 39, 44, 47,
   49, 50, 59, 61, 63,
   69, 72, 75, 85

U.S. Department of
  Agriculture, 28
University of California,
  21, 46
University of Colorado, 59
University of Guadalajara,
  Mexico, 46
University of Nottingham,
  England, 84

V Vavilov Centers, 30-31
Vavilov, Nikolai, 30, 63
Venezuela, 53
Victoria blight, 53
vinblastine, 73
vincristine, 73
Vogel, Dr. Orville, 44

W Walbot, Dr. Virginia, 84
Watson, Dr. James D., 41
wheat, 11, 12, 30, 32,
  44-45, 63, 84-85
wheat blight, 21
Wisconsin Potato Station,
  63
World Wildlife Fund, 76

Z *Zea diploperennis* (Z-dip,
  ancient maize,
  teosinte), 47

About the Authors

Margery and Howard Facklam have collaborated on a number of nonfiction books for young people. Both authors have extensive backgrounds in science and education.

Margery has been the Curator of Education at the Aquarium of Niagara Falls, the Assistant Administrator of Education at the Buffalo Museum of Science, and the Education Coordinator of the Buffalo Zoo. She now enjoys being a full-time writer.

Howard has been a teacher of biology and chemistry for over thirty years. He attended Cornell University and the State University of New York at Buffalo. After pursuing a career in the insurance industry, he returned to college for graduate work in chemistry and biology in order to become a teacher, a profession he truly loves.

Margery and Howard Facklam have five grown children. One son, Paul, is an artist and has done illustrations for several of their books, including *Plants: Extinction or Survival*.